SECOND SERIES

More Classics to Moderns

Compiled and edited by Denes Agay

It is with pleasure that we present More Classics To Moderns. It is a sequel to our now widely used Classics To Moderns.

Because of the extended period of music history in both books, beginning pianists of all ages will discover material well suited to their needs. This material is easy enough to be used by the beginning student as his first sight reading book. At the university level, the student will find a rich source of reference to supplement his study of theory and composition.

The original compositions selected by Denes Agay involved extensive research covering the piano literature of more than three centuries. There is a wide representation of composers, including some of the lesser known masters, all of whom the player will be delighted to encounter.

All selections are in their original form, neither re-arranged nor simplified. They appear in approximately chronological order. Marks of phrasing and expression are often editorial additions, especially in the music of the pre-classic period. These signs were added for a quicker and easier understanding of the structure and mood of the compositions. They are to be considered as suggestions rather than rigid directions.

Students, teachers and all pianists will find these original miniatures valuable for study, recital, sight reading or just relaxing musical entertainment of the highest calibre. *The Publishers*

Yorktown Music Press
London/New York/Sydney/Tokyo/Cologne

£3·95

Exclusive distributors
Music Sales Limited
78 Newman Street, London W1P 3LA, England.
Music Sales Pty. Limited
27 Clarendon Street, Artarmon, Sydney, NSW 2064, Australia.
Music Sales Corporation
24 East 22nd Street, New York, N.Y. 10010, USA.

This book ©Copyright 1979 by
Yorktown Music Press
ISBN 0.86001.682X
Order No. YK 20170

Music Sales complete catalogue lists thousands of
titles and is free from your local music book shop,
or direct from Music Sales Limited.
Please send 30p in stamps for postage to
Music Sales Limited, 78 Newman Street, London W1P 3LA.

Printed in England by
J. B. Offset Printers (Marks Tey) Limited, Marks Tey.

CONTENTS

Concerto
(1st Movement)

George Frideric Handel
(1685-1759)

* Tempo and dynamic marks are editorial additions.

© 1974 Consolidated Music Publishers, Inc.

Bourrée
from *French Overture*

Johann Sebastian Bach
(1685-1750)

* All crotchets may be played staccato.

Alla Turca
from *Sonata K.331*

Wolfgang Amadeus Mozart
(1756-1791)

F♯ in some editions.

Scherzo
from Sonata Op.2, No.2

Ludwig van Beethoven
(1770-1827)

Scherzo D.C.

*According to the earliest edition. In the autograph the 1st beat is a rest;
the G follows on the second beat. Probably Beethoven's own correction.

Moment Musical

Op.94, No.6

Franz Schubert
(1797–1828)

Trio

Allegretto D.C.

Song Without Words

Boat Song

Felix Mendelssohn-Bartholdy
(1809-1847)

Allegretto, non troppo

Friendly Landscape

from Forest Scenes, Op.82, No.5

Robert Schumann
(1810–1856)

Waltz
Op.70, No.2

Frédéric Chopin
(1819-1849)

* At FINE the middle note of this chord should be omitted.

D.S. 𝄋 al Fine

Malagueña

from "España" Op.165,No.3

Isaac Albeniz
(1860–1909)

Allegretto

D.C. al Fine

Danseuses de Delphes
from Preludes, Book 1

Claude Debussy
(1862–1918)

Prelude

Op.38, No.23

Dmitri Kabalevsky
(1906-   )

Andante sostenuto

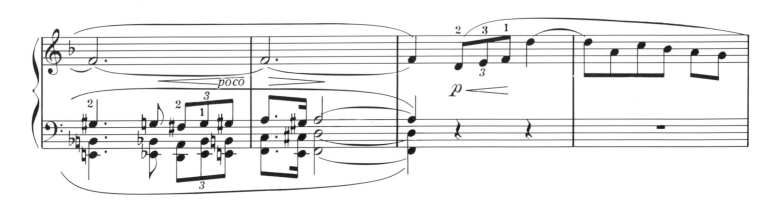

Armenian Dance

Aram Khatchaturian
(1904-   )

Allegro non troppo; marcato (♩.=84 -92)

D.C. al Fine

Picnic
From "Sports et Divertissements"

Erik Satie
(1866-1925)

Like a dance

Everybody has brought cold veal.

You are wearing a lovely white dress.

Oh my! An airplane!

Not at all: it's a storm coming up.